MEET THE FLYING REPTILES

by Rebecca Donnelly
illustrated by Alan Brown

GRASSHOPPER

Tools for Parents & Teachers

Grasshopper Books enhance imagination and introduce the earliest readers to fiction with fun storylines and illustrations. The easy-to-read text supports early reading experiences with repetitive sentence patterns and sight words.

Before Reading

- Discuss the cover illustration. What do they see?

- Look at the glossary together. Discuss the words.

Read the Book

- Read the book to the child, or have him or her read independently.

- "Walk" through the book and look at the illustrations. What is happening in the story?

After Reading

- Prompt the child to think more. Ask: In what ways are pterosaurs similar to birds? In what ways are they different? How are they similar to or different from dinosaurs?

Grasshopper Books are published by Jump!
5357 Penn Avenue South
Minneapolis, MN 55419
www.jumplibrary.com

Library of Congress Cataloging-in-Publication Data

Names: Donnelly, Rebecca, author.
Brown, Alan, illustrator.
Title: Meet the flying reptiles / Rebecca Donnelly; illustrated by Alan Brown.
Description: Minneapolis, MN: Jump!, Inc., [2022]
Series: Meet the dinosaurs!: when reptiles ruled
Includes index.
Audience: Ages 7-10
Identifiers: LCCN 2021038051 (print)
LCCN 2021038052 (ebook)
ISBN 9781636906058 (hardcover)
ISBN 9781636906065 (paperback)
ISBN 9781636906072 (ebook)
Subjects: LCSH: Dinosaurs–Flight–Juvenile literature.
Classification: LCC QE861.6.F45 D66 2022 (print)
LCC QE861.6.F45 (ebook)
DDC 567.918–dc23
LC record available at https://lccn.loc.gov/2021038051
LC ebook record available at https://lccn.loc.gov/2021038052

Editor: Eliza Leahy
Direction and Layout: Anna Peterson
Illustrator: Alan Brown

Printed in the United States of America at Corporate Graphics in North Mankato, Minnesota.

Table of Contents

Hi, I'm Tara the Pteranodon! I'm a pterosaur. We aren't dinosaurs, but we lived at the same time as them. Unlike most dinosaurs, we can fly!

bill

My wings are 20 feet (6.1 meters) across! I fly over the water and grab fish with my bill. *Whoosh!* Let's meet some other flying reptiles!

Come fly with me, Teresa the Tropeognathus. My long, thin wings are more than 26 feet (7.9 m) across! I'm a piscivore, like Tara. I use my wings to glide while I hunt for fish. My sharp teeth help me snatch my dinner out of the water!

I'm Tomás the Pterodaustro. My wingspan is 8 feet (2.4 m). I'm smaller than Teresa, but I have something she doesn't.

I have more than 1,000 tiny teeth in my bill! I use them to strain brine shrimp and small crustaceans from the water. Yum!

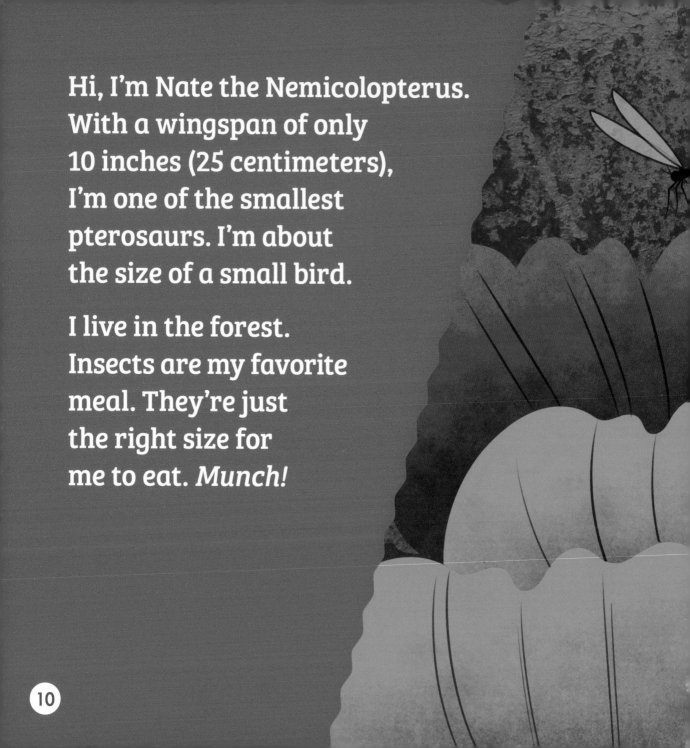

Hi, I'm Nate the Nemicolopterus. With a wingspan of only 10 inches (25 centimeters), I'm one of the smallest pterosaurs. I'm about the size of a small bird.

I live in the forest. Insects are my favorite meal. They're just the right size for me to eat. *Munch!*

Shh! I'm Hana the Hamipterus. This is my nest. I'm covering my eggs in mud to protect them from predators. When the eggs hatch, I'll bring food to my babies. When they get older, they'll learn to fly and catch fish.

egg

I'm David. I'm a Dimorphodon. My wingspan is 4.5 feet (1.4 m). I can fly, but when I'm on the ground, I walk on my hands and feet. All pterosaurs do this.

I'm a good climber, too.
I see dinner on that rock!
Watch me get it!

Hi! I'm Amir the Afrotapejara. It's lunchtime, so I'm going fishing.

See this crest on my bill? It's how members of my species recognize one another.

crest

17

Did someone say crest?
I'm Telma the Tupandactylus.
Check out my crest! It's the
biggest of any pterosaur.
I fly, but I don't eat fish.
I'm an herbivore. I use
my bill to pluck yummy
fruits off plants.

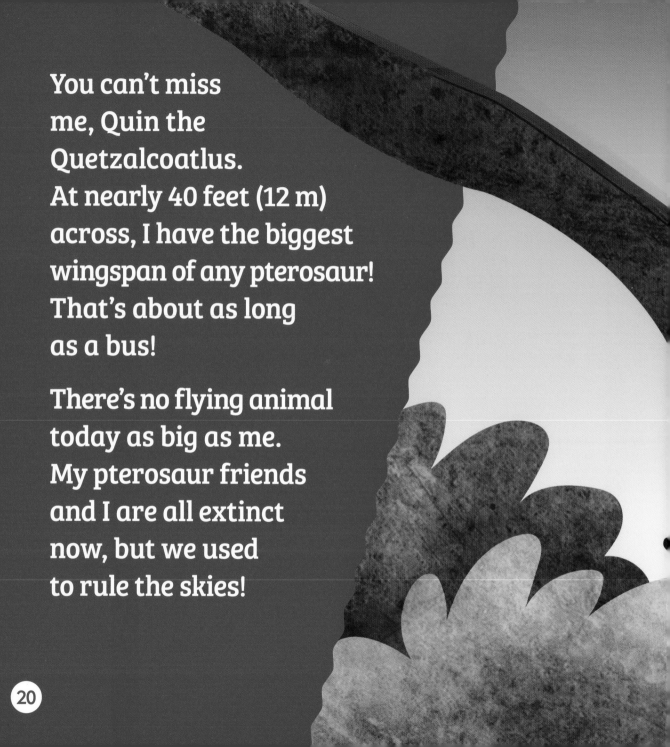

You can't miss
me, Quin the
Quetzalcoatlus.
At nearly 40 feet (12 m)
across, I have the biggest
wingspan of any pterosaur!
That's about as long
as a bus!

There's no flying animal
today as big as me.
My pterosaur friends
and I are all extinct
now, but we used
to rule the skies!

Timeline

Dinosaurs lived millions of years ago.
Take a look at when the dinosaurs in this
book lived!

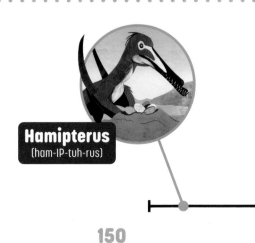

Hamipterus
(ham-IP-tuh-rus)

200 MILLION YEARS AGO (MYA)   **175**   **150**

JURASSIC PERIOD 200–145 MYA

Dimorphodon
(dye-MOR-foh-don)

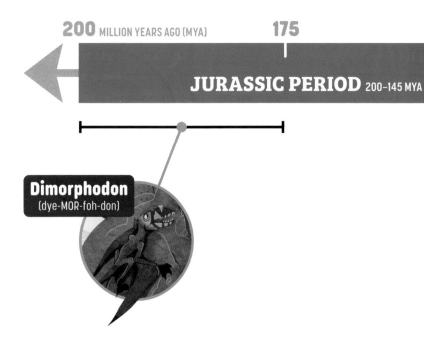

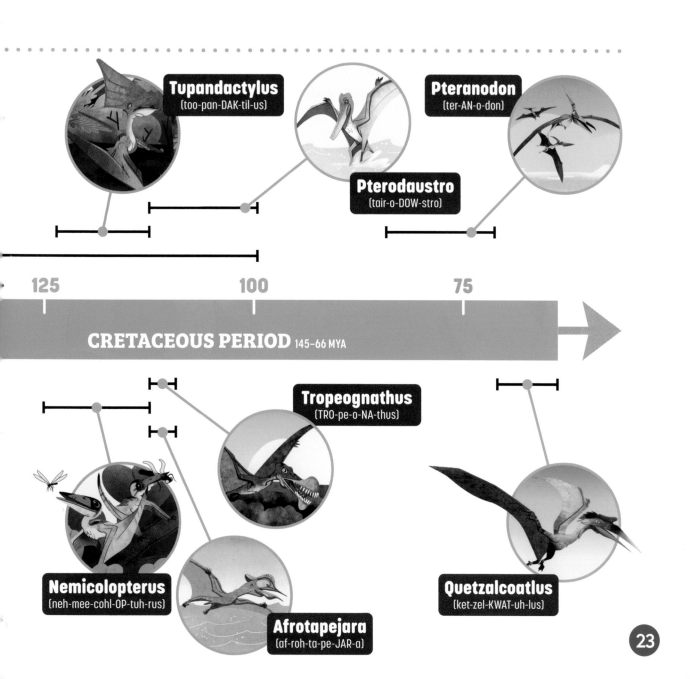

Tupandactylus
(too-pan-DAK-til-us)

Pterodaustro
(tair-o-DOW-stro)

Pteranodon
(ter-AN-o-don)

Tropeognathus
(TRO-pe-o-NA-thus)

Nemicolopterus
(neh-mee-cohl-OP-tuh-rus)

Afrotapejara
(af-roh-ta-pe-JAR-a)

Quetzalcoatlus
(ket-zel-KWAT-uh-lus)

125
100
75

CRETACEOUS PERIOD 145–66 MYA

Glossary

crustaceans: Sea creatures that have outer skeletons, such as crabs, lobsters, and shrimp.

extinct: No longer found alive and known about only through fossils or history.

flying reptiles: Extinct animals with bird-like beaks and wings that lived during the time of the dinosaurs.

herbivore: An animal that eats plants.

piscivore: An animal that eats fish.

predators: Animals that hunt other animals for food.

pterosaur: A type of winged prehistoric reptile not related to birds or dinosaurs.

species: One of the groups into which similar animals and plants are divided.

strain: To pass through as if through a strainer.

wingspan: The distance from the tip of one wing to the tip of the other.

Index

To Learn More

Finding more information is as easy as 1, 2, 3.

❶ Go to www.factsurfer.com

❷ Enter "**meettheflyingreptiles**" into the search box.

❸ Choose your book to see a list of websites.

FACT SURFER